V74A
Accompaniment Edition

SING LEGATO

A Collection of Original Studies in Vocal Production and Musicianship

by Kenneth Jennings

ISBN 0-8497-4159-9

Neil A. Kjos Music Company, San Diego, California

CONTENTS

VOCALISES   Page

  1. Sing Legato 4

  2. Staccato Is Short 7

  3. Marcato Is Strong 8

  4. Rich Tone 10

  5. Sing a Little Louder 12

  6. Sigh the Tone 14

  7. Flexibility 16

INTERVAL SONGS

  8. Whole Step, Half Step 19

  9. The Third Comes in Two Sizes 22

10. Fourths and Fifths Go Up and Down 26

11. Gliding Along (Sixths) 28

12. Seconds and Sevenths 32

13. The Octave Leap 34

STAFF LINES FOR ADDITIONAL VOCALISES . . .39

INTRODUCTION

This brief set of vocal studies is designed for the individual voice student and for use in voice classes and choral groups. The vocalises are set as short songs emphasizing basic aspects of what the solo or ensemble singer encounters in music. The texts are to help the students remember better what is communicated in the studio and rehearsal room and to serve as an aid in the development of musicianship.

The purpose is not to provide a text on vocal technique or methods. It is rather to provide for the student and teacher some vocal materials that are adaptable to various levels of vocal development for both individual and ensemble use.

The opening VOCALISES focus on basic kinds of musical articulations: legato, staccato, and marcato. Numbers 4 and 6 aid in the development of good tone and an even use of the breath. Number 5 gives practice in crescendo and decrescendo, and Number 7 is an exercise in flexibility.

The INTERVAL SONGS, Numbers 8 to 13, emphasize interval recognition aurally and visually, and provide melodies and texts that can be used for their potential as vocal learning materials. In purpose and design, they are reminiscent of the interval vocalises by the famous early nineteenth century Italian voice teacher, Nicola Vaccai.

The order of the pieces is flexible. Students and teachers should begin with those exercises that are most compatible with the student's vocal development. Several transpositions are provided for each vocalise. Accompaniments can be simplified (see the transpositions) to help the singer achieve independence of the vocal line.

In voice classes and choral groups, alternation of phrases and exercises between men and women, section and tutti, solo and group, or between soloists gives variety and the opportunity to listen and learn from others. These vocalises have been used with good results by students from grade school through college. They can also be used as group "warm-ups." Use them imaginatively!

It is important to remember that the following all contribute to good singing:

- good posture
- a poised, alert body
- breathing that fills to the bottom of the lungs
- a loose jaw
- free shoulder and neck muscles
- good vocal energy
- focus and beauty of tone
- understandable diction
- an alert ear
- good intonation
- a consistent goal of singing musically and tastefully

I hope these short songs will be an aid in this process.

— Kenneth Jennings
Conductor, St. Olaf Choir

1. SING LEGATO

- Be sure to slur the vowel (see the first bar) when it occurs on two or more pitches.
- Avoid "h's" or hops between pitches!
- Between the last two phrases (from "oh" to "smoothly"), feel that the upper note sings from the same place as the lower.
- Sing moderately fast.
- Sing four bars on one breath, and eventually, eight.

©1982 Neil A. Kjos Music Co., San Diego, Calif.
Inter. Copyright Secured   All Rights Reserved   Printed in U.S.A.

SING LEGATO, transpositions

V74A
Accompaniment Edition
$3.45

SING LEGATO

A Collection of Original Studies in Vocal Production and Musicianship

by Kenneth Jennings

kjos   Neil A. Kjos Music Company, San Diego, California

2. STACCATO IS SHORT

- Sing staccatos with a light tone and with short rather than accented notes.
- Sing with inner excitement, but save the accents for the Marcato (3).
  (The Marcato may directly follow the Staccato.)

Stac - ca - to   is   short   and   snap -

py.   Stac - ca - to   is   short   as   notes   can   be!

3. MARCATO IS STRONG

- Sing with accents but in a sustained and connected fashion.
- Sing with a full tone, **forte**.

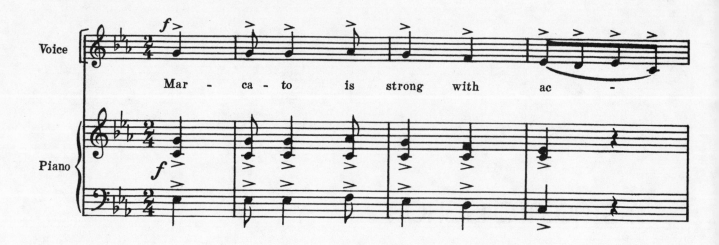

Mar - ca - to is strong with ac -

cents. We sing with strength and deep _____ tone.
full _____
fo - cused
point - ed

STACCATO AND MARCATO, transpositions

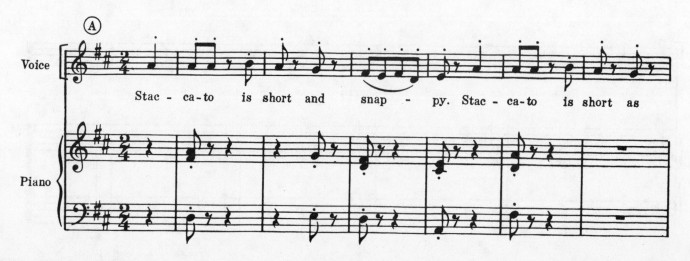

Stac - ca - to is short and snap - py. Stac - ca - to is short as

4. RICH TONE

- Sing very legato and beautifully.
- Keep your jaw loose. (Can you move it from side to side a bit without changing tone?)
- Feel your breath evenly without bursts on changes of pitches or words.
- Use the alternate words suggested or make up your own.

1. Rich _____ tone with o - pen throat,
2. Sigh _____ the tone with loos - ened jaw,
3. Sing _____ a song with loos - ened jaw,

Rich _____ tone _____ on e - ven breath.
Sigh _____ the tone _____ on e - ven breath.
Sing _____ a song _____ on e - ven breath.

RICH TONE, transpositions

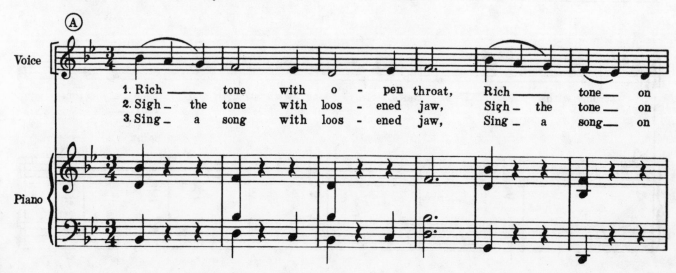

1. Rich _____ tone with o - pen throat, Rich _____ tone _____ on
2. Sigh _ the tone with loos - ened jaw, Sigh _ the tone _____ on
3. Sing _ a song with loos - ened jaw, Sing _ a song _____ on

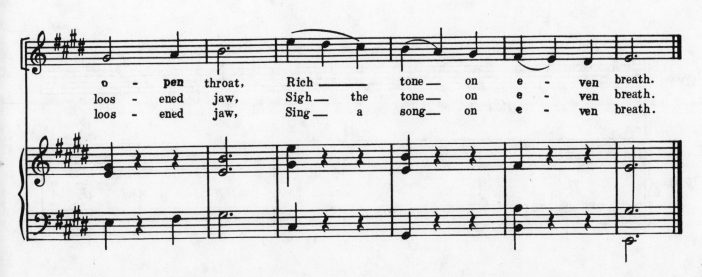

5. SING A LITTLE LOUDER

- Start softly; add more fullness to your voice as you sing louder.
- Lighten your voice and decrescendo as you sing down the scale. (This vocalise may also be sung in minor.)

SING A LITTLE LOUDER, transpositions

Sing a lit-tle soft - er in de - cre-scen-dos with a light-er voice.

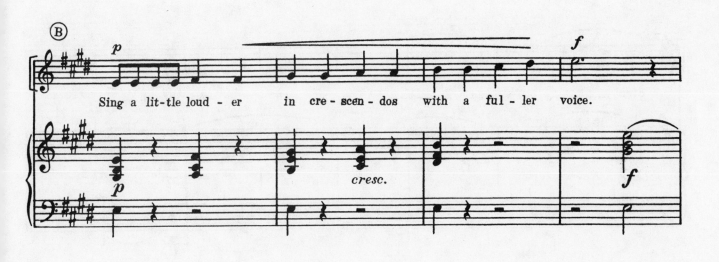

Ⓑ Sing a lit-tle loud - er in cre - scen - dos with a ful - ler voice.

Sing a lit-tle soft - er in de - cre-scen - dos with a light-er voice.

6. SIGH THE TONE

- Slur on the words "sigh" and "smile," feeling the voice a bit lighter on the lower pitches.
- Imagine the "smile" inside, especially on the "ah-ee" diphthong.

Sigh_ the tone, sigh_ the tone with a smile_ in - side; _____

Sigh, _____ smile _____ on an e - ven breath. _____

SIGH THE TONE, transpositions

Ⓐ

Sigh_ the tone, sigh_ the tone with a smile_ in -

7. FLEXIBLITY

- Repeat the vowel on the slurred notes ("fleh-eh-eh") like a quick, happy chuckle. (Surprisingly this is easier to do quickly than slowly. Do not be overly concerned about accuracy at first.)
- Keep your voice light.

FLEXIBILITY, transpositions

18

8. WHOLE STEPS, HALF STEPS

- Alternate major and minor phrases between men and women, teacher and student, or one student and another.
- Imagine the scale steps slightly larger when ascending and somewhat smaller when descending.
- Hear the differences in the arrangement of half and whole steps when the music changes from major to minor.

WHOLE STEP, HALF STEP, transpositions

Ⓑ

Whole step, whole step, half step, then whole step; Half step, whole step,

simile

whole step and half a-gain; Whole, whole, half step, whole steps;

Whole, half, whole step, whole, half; Whole step, whole step,

half step, then whole step; Half step, whole step, whole step and half a - gain.

9. THE THIRD COMES IN TWO SIZES

- Be aware of the importance of thirds in many melodies. A series of them together in the same direction outlines a chord. (Notice the first phrase.)
- Sing this vocalise with enthusiasm.
- Alternate phrases between singers.

tween; the mi - nor is a half step less as ev' - ry one can

hear! _____ The third comes in two siz - es: (MA - JOR)

mi - nor, (mi - nor) MA - JOR, (mi - nor) MA - JOR, mi - nor thirds.

THE THIRD COMES IN TWO SIZES, transpositions

The third comes in two siz-es: mi-nor and MA-JOR, MA-JOR, mi-nor

thirds. The thirds. The MA-JOR third may come an-y-where with two steps in be-

tween; the mi-nor is a half step less as ev'-ry one can hear! The

third comes in two siz-es: (MA-JOR) mi-nor, (mi-nor) MA-JOR, (mi-nor) MA-JOR, mi-nor thirds.

10. FOURTHS AND FIFTHS GO UP AND DOWN

- Sing smoothly and gently.
- Sing the whole text on a single repeated note first, very legato.
- Keep the legato when you add melody.
- Use enough good vocal energy and breath so that all the pitches feel
  like the same voice quality.

Fourths and fifths go up and down, Fifths and fourths de - scend or rise;

per - fect in - ter - vals by name, sing with care what - ev - er size:

down a fourth, up a fourth; down a fifth, up once more.

FOURTHS AND FIFTHS GO UP AND DOWN, transpositions

11. GLIDING ALONG (Sixths)

- Feel the breath and tone like a skater's long strides.
- Remember that wider ranges, leaps, and longer phrases all require good vocal energy and flowing breath.

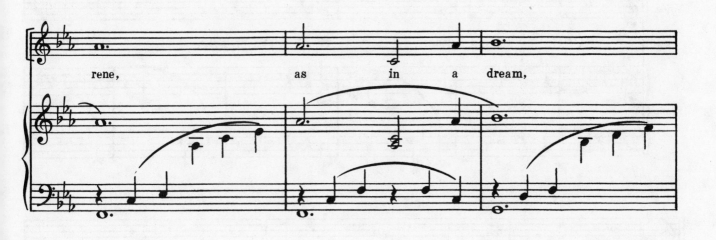

rene, as in a dream,

our voic - es raise in hymns of praise,

sixths glide on wings of song.

GLIDING ALONG, transpositions

Glid - ing a - long on wings of song, we lift our
voic - es and re - joice; Smooth and se - rene,
as in a dream, our voic - es raise in hymns of
praise, sixths _____ glide _____ on wings of song.

12. SECONDS AND SEVENTHS

- Keep in mind that seconds and sevenths are related intervals. Melodies
    using these intervals often have two pitch centers, one high and
    one low.
- Hear the melody clearly in your imagination as you alternate between
    the two pitch areas.
- Sing with good energy and feel all the pitches centered in your voice,
    whether you are singing the higher or lower group of notes.

SECONDS AND SEVENTHS, transpositions

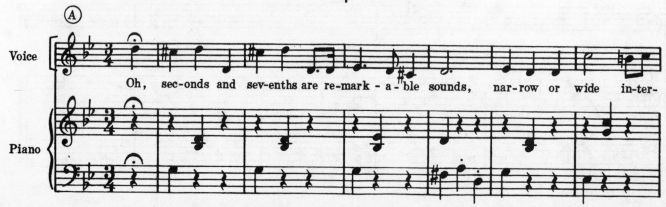

vals they___ are. Wide___ or nar-row, far___ or near, sev-enths or

seconds, sing sweet and clear. Oh, sec-onds and sev-enths are re-mark-a-ble

sounds, nar-row or wide in-ter-vals they___ are. Wide___ or nar-row,

far___ or near, sev-enths or sec-onds, sing sweet and clear.

13. THE OCTAVE LEAP

- As with Seconds and Sevenths, feel all the pitches centered in your voice.
- Sing the phrases with good energy and with a light marcato approach.

Voice / Piano

The oc - tave leap is a sud - den one, Ah - ee - ah - ee - oh.

Oc - tave leaps can bring sur - prise, Ah - ee - ah - ee - oh. The

range is rath - er wide you see; Takes both skill and en - er - gy to

sing the leap ac-cur-ate-ly, Ah - ee - oh - ah! ——— The
oc - tave leap we all sur-mise Takes the list'-ning skills we
prize ——————— To sing ex - act - ly
oc - tave - wise.

THE OCTAVE LEAP, transpositions

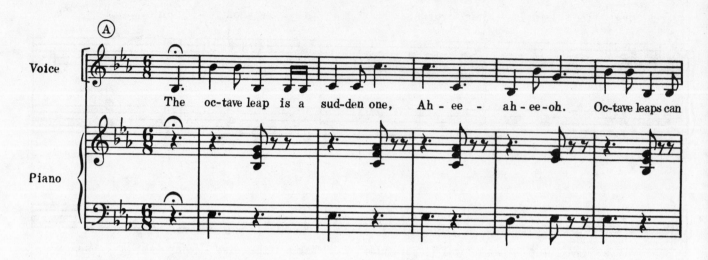

Voice

Piano

The oc-tave leap is a sud-den one, Ah - ee - ah - ee - oh. Oc-tave leaps can

bring sur-prise, Ah - ee - ah - ee - oh. The range is rath - er wide you see;

Takes both skill and en - er - gy to sing the leap ac-cur-ate-ly, Ah - ee - oh -

ah!___ The oc-tave leap we all sur-mise Takes the list'-ning skills we

prize _____ To sing ex - act - ly oc -

- tave - wise. The oc-tave leap is a sud-den one,

Ah - ee - ah -ee-oh. Oc-tave leaps can bring sur-prise, Ah - ee -

ah — ee — oh. The range is rath-er wide you see; Takes both skill and en-er-gy to

sing the leap ac-cur-ate-ly, Ah - ee - oh - ah!____ The oc-tave leap we

all sur-mise Takes the list'- ning skills we prize _____ To

sing ex - act-ly oc - tave - wise.

ADDITIONAL VOCALISES

ADDITIONAL VOCALISES